A **MURDER CAN BE FATAL** MYSTERY

SIX MILLION WAYS TO DIE

ALAN NOLAN

THE O'BRIEN PRESS

FOR HOLLY, JACK, KATIE AND HANNAH

First published 2011 by The O'Brien Press Ltd
12 Terenure Road East, Rathgar, Dublin 6, Ireland
Tel: +353 1 4923333; Fax: +353 1 4292777
Email: books @ obrien.ie
Website: www.obrien.ie

ISBN: 978-1-84717-255-6
Copyright for text, illustrations and layout design © Alan Nolan 2011

A catalogue record for this title is available from the British Library

1 2 3 4 5 6
11 12 13 14

The O'Brien Press receives assistance from

Editing: The O'Brien Press Ltd
Printed by CPI Anthony Rowe Ltd
The paper used in this book is produced using pulp from managed forests

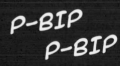

P-BIP
P-BIP

4

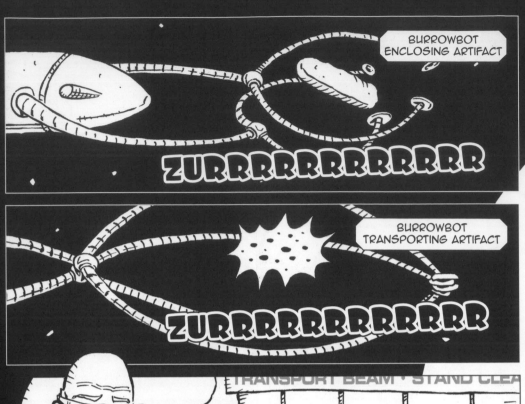

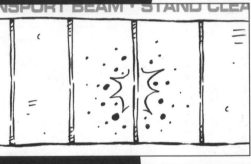

8

13

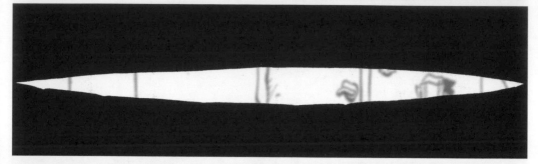

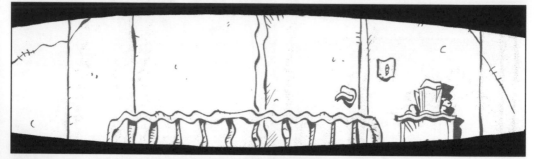

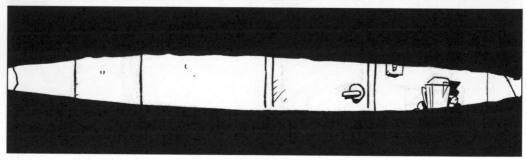

AW, MAN...

15

SUSHI BOWL NOO FRESH

FELIX'S APARTMENT BUILDING AT LAST.

I'M GOING UP TO SEE FELIX SILVERBERG ON THE 9TH.

SAY, WHERE'S LOUIE, THE REGULAR DOORMAN?

LOUIE? SORRY SIR, I'VE BEEN WORKING HERE FOR FOUR YEARS, I DON'T KNOW NO LOUIE.

22

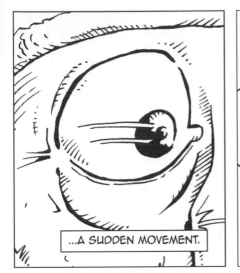

...A SUDDEN MOVEMENT.

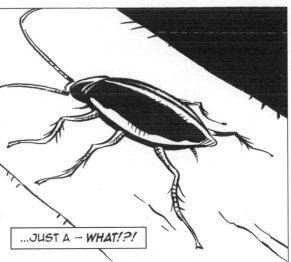

...JUST A — *WHAT!?!*

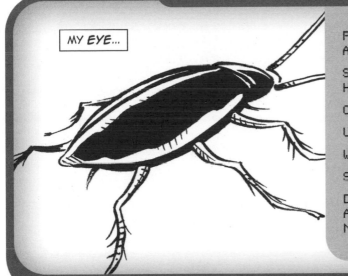

MY *EYE*...

PHYLUM: ARTHROPODA

SUBPHYLUM: HEXAPODAA

CLASS: INSECTA

LENGTH: 3.73CM

WEIGHT: 22.7G

SPEED: 4.5 KMPH

DANGER TO ALDRIN SUBJECT: N/A

IT'S... *BIOTRONIC!!*

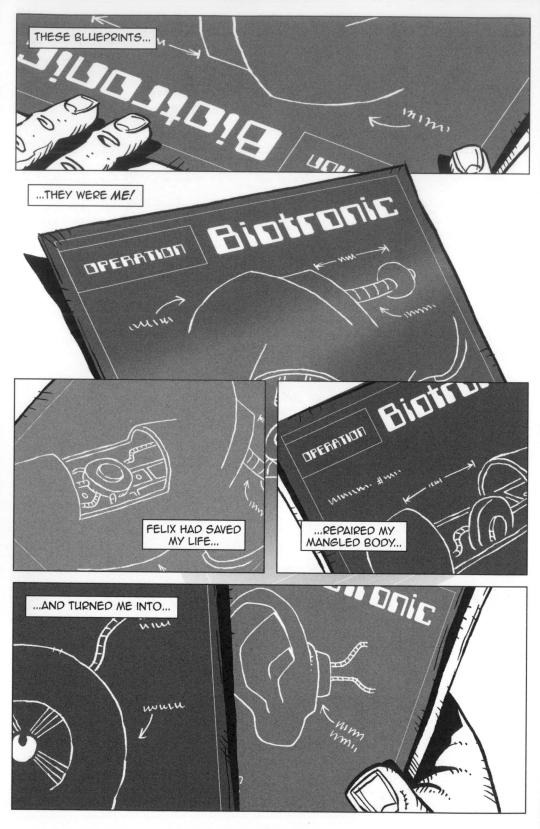

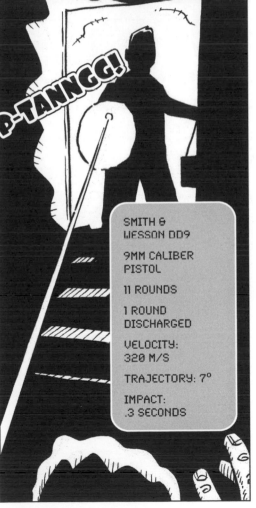

29

31

33

WAIT! ...WHAT'S THAT?

MORE INSANITY!

ALBANY TIMES

THURSDAY

APRIL. 18, 1912

TITANIC

CROSSES ATLANTIC IN RECORD TIME

DOCKED IN NEW YORK WEDNESDAY

EVERYONE KNOWS *THE TITANIC* NEVER MADE IT TO NEW YORK!

IT *SANK* ON ITS MAIDEN VOYAGE...

THE 'UNSINKABLE' TITANIC HIT AN ICE-BERG AND SANK.

A THOUSAND PEOPLE PERISHED IN THE ICY NORTH ATLANTIC.

BUT NOT IN *THIS* REALITY. NOT IN THIS—

WHAT?!?

FELIX?!?

THE CAPTION READ 'MIDSHIPMAN THEODORE SILVERBERG AND PASSENGER'

THIS WAS *TOO* WEIRD.

I HAD TO GET BACK TO THE APARTMENT.

IN ALL THIS CRAZINESS, AT LEAST ONE THING WAS CERTAIN...

RMS TITANIC

...I WAS *OUT OF TIME.*

AHEM. *SIR?*

I'M AFRAID THERE IS A *DRESS CODE* ON THE FIRST CLASS DECK.

EH... OF COURSE.

EXCUSE ME.

WAIT. WHAT *DATE* IS IT?

THE DATE? *14TH APRIL,* SIR. SUNDAY.

14TH APRIL! TONIGHT THIS SHIP *HITS AN ICEBERG — AND SINKS!*

I HAD TO FIND FELIX, AND *FAST!*

42

43

44

PLEASE KEEP THIS TO YOURSELF, MR ALDRIN, BUT THERE HAVE BEEN *TWO MURDERS* ABOARD THIS SHIP SINCE WE LEFT QUEENSTOWN

FIRST A MAN FROM THIRD CLASS, THEN ONE OF THE POOR WAITERS.

AND THE KILLER IS STILL ON THE LOOSE?

WHY DON'T THEY TURN THE SHIP AROUND?

BECAUSE THE WHITE STAR LINE DOESN'T WANT THE SCANDAL.

THE *TITANIC* IS THE FASTEST SHIP IN THE WORLD, A MIRACLE OF MODERN SCIENCE AND COMPLETELY *UNSINKABLE*.

SO THEY *SAY*...

TWO MURDERS WOULD BRING THE SHIP AND THE COMPANY INTO *DISREPUTE*.

AND THESE DAYS REP-UTATION IS *EVERYTHING*.

AND GIVEN THAT WE ARE IN THE MIDDLE OF THE NORTH ATLANTIC OCEAN, IT WOULD SEEM THE KILLER IS GOING *NOWHERE*.

HE IS *TRAPPED*.

AND *WE* IN TURN ARE *TRAPPED HERE WITH HIM*.

OF COURSE!

REALLY! I AM GLAD TO HEAR THAT.

IT IS NOT MUCH USED OUTSIDE THE UNITED STATES, AND EVEN THEN MOST STATES DO NOT ALLOW IT AS EVIDENCE.

NATURALLY, MR MCGARRETT AND THE CAPTAIN WON'T HEAR ME OUT.

THEY DON'T THINK IT'S A WOMAN'S PLACE TO GET INVOLVED IN SOMETHING SO SORDID AS *MURDER.*

BUT WOMEN IN MY HOME COUNTRY SHALL SOON HAVE *THE VOTE*, MR ALDRIN.

TITANIC

AND WHEN WE *DO*, WE SHALL *SEE* IF CONGRESSMAN MCGARRETT *GETS RE-ELECTED!*

WOW, I FORGOT! IT WAS 1912, WOMEN DIDN'T HAVE THE VOTE IN THE UNITED STATES, OR IN THE UNITED KINGDOM FOR THAT MATTER.

I'M ALL FOR EQUALITY, MISS FARADAY.

THANK YOU, MR ALDRIN.

CALL ME REX.

THIS GIRL WAS *SMART.* AND ONE TOUGH COOKIE TO STAND UP TO THE OWNERS AND THE CAPTAIN LIKE THAT.

I LIKED HER STRAIGHT AWAY.

49

51

SO THERE I WAS, LOCKED UP WHILE MCGARRETT FIGURED OUT WHAT TO DO WITH ME.

THE WAY I SAW IT HE HAD TWO CHOICES; EITHER KEEP ME LOCKED UP UNTIL WE DOCK IN NEW YORK (OR HIT THE ICEBERG...)

OR MAKE ME *WALK THE PLANK.*

THAT DARN *CELL PHONE* WAS NO GOOD TO ME BACK IN 1912.

HMMM. CONGRESSMAN MCGARRETT...

MCGARRETT! I KNEW I'D HEARD THAT NAME BEFORE! IN THOSE OLD NEWS CLIPPINGS – *HE BECOMES PRESIDENT!*

GOSHDARNIT, MAYBE IF THIS SHIP *DOESN'T SINK,* MCGARRETT WILL *LIVE* AND END UP *RUNNING* THAT WEIRD *JAPANESE U.S. HYBRID GOVERNMENT!*

MAY I SPEAK TO MR ALDRIN, PLEASE?

MR ALDRIN?

CALL ME REX.

REX, I *DON'T BELIEVE* YOU MURDERED THAT MAN.

53

59

YES, REX, *GREAT GREAT UNCLE THEODORE.* THE *INK BLOT* ON THE SILVERBERG FAMILY'S COPYBOOK.

EVERY FAMILY HAS ITS *BLACK SHEEP*, BUT FEW ARE AS BLACK AS THEODORE.

AND FOND OF THE *BOTTLE.*

THEY PACKED HIM OFF TO THE MERCHANT NAVY. TO MAKE A *MAN* OF HIM.

DIDN'T WORK.

DISHONOURABLE DISCHARGE. DRUNK ON DUTY.

HE DRIFTED. SINGAPORE. INDIA.

FROM CRUMMY JOB TO CRUMMY JOB.

HIS DRINKING GOT WORSE.

THEN HE HAD A *STROKE OF LUCK...*

MIDSHIPMAN ON THE *TITANIC!*

THE FAMILY WERE DELIGHTED. A *GOOD JOB* WITH A *REPUTABLE COMPANY*....

...THEY HOPED IT WOULD BE THE MAKING OF HIM.

...BUT IT TURNED OUT TO BE THE *UNDOING* OF OUR FAMILY.

YOU SEE, ON THAT FATEFUL NIGHT, THE 14TH OF APRIL, 1912 — *TONIGHT* —

...*THEODORE* WAS ON *LOOKOUT DUTY.*

THERE HAD BEEN REPORTS FROM OTHER VESSELS IN THE AREA.

REPORTS OF *ICEBERGS.*

THE NORTH ATLANTIC IS A DESOLATE, COLD PLACE.

WHO KNOWS?

MAYBE TO WARM UP HE TOOK A SIP OF RUM.

MAYBE BEFORE HE KNEW IT HE HAD DRUNK THE WHOLE BOTTLE.

69

EPILOGUE...